Dear SpongeBob...

A Funny Fill-ins Book

by Steven Banks

SCHOLASTIC INC.

New York   Toronto   London   Auckland   Sydney
Mexico City   New Delhi   Hong Kong   Buenos Aires

Based on the TV series *SpongeBob SquarePants*®
created by Stephen Hillenburg as seen on Nickelodeon®

ISBN 0-439-53974-9

12 11 10 9 8 7   8/0

Printed in the U.S.A.

First Scholastic printing, September 2003

Hi! It's me, SpongeBob SquarePants! I get a lot of letters asking important questions and I need your help answering them. Are you ready? Here's what you do . . .

Pick a friend to write words in the blanks. He or she will not read the letters out loud until all the blanks have been filled in. The other friend (or friends) will give him or her the words.

When asked for a NOUN, fill in the name of a person, place, or thing. *Clam, seaweed,* and *bucket* are examples of nouns.

When asked for a VERB, fill in an action word. *Eat, wrestle,* and *honk* are examples of verbs. You'll also be asked for an "-ing verb." This means words like *eating, wrestling,* and *honking.* Sometimes you'll be asked for a "past-tense verb." *Ate, wrestled,* and *honked* are examples of past-tense verb.

An ADJECTIVE is a word that describes a person or a thing, like *pretty, amazing,* or *horrible.*

An ADVERB is a word that describes how something is done, and usually ends with "ly," like *quickly, shyly,* and *seriously.*

You'll also be asked for specific words like "type of food," "type of sea creature," or "number." Just fill in a word that's one of those things.

That's it! I'm ready—let's go!

Dear SpongeBob,

I have a huge problem. I can't sleep at night. Every time I go to bed I hear a noise that sounds like a(n) _____ trying to swallow

type of animal

a(n) _____ :

noun

Help!

Signed,
Sleepless in
Bikini Bottom

4

Dear Sleepless in Bikini Bottom,

That's just my friend Squidward playing his clarinet! I suggest putting _____
_{type of lunch meat}
in your ears or wearing a(n)_____ over
_{noun}
your head. If this doesn't work, drink a(n)_____-flavored glass of warm _____.
_{noun}   _{type of liquid}
You can also try counting_____s
_{type of sea creature}
jumping over_____s. That always works
_{noun}
for me!

Sweet dreams!

Sleepily yours,

SpongeBob SquarePants

Dear SpongeBob,

I get very nervous when I have to take a test at school. The minute I sit down at my

_____, my mind goes
     noun

_____, and I forget
  adjective

everything I _____.
              past-tense verb

At this rate, I'll be in summer school for the next_____
                extremely high number

years!

What can I do?

Signed,

Summer-School Bound

Dear Summer-School Bound,

I know how you feel! Whenever I take a test at Mrs. Puff's Boating School my _____ gets
body part

sweaty and my _____ shakes. Sometimes
body part

I can't remember the answers, so I just guess or put down the number_____. The last time I took
number

my driving test I ran over a(n)_____,
noun

crashed into a(n) _____, and then drove back
noun

to school so slowly that an old _____
type of sea creature

passed me. But someday I will pass the test and become a(n)_____ driver!
adjective

Studiously yours,

**SpongeBob
SquarePants**

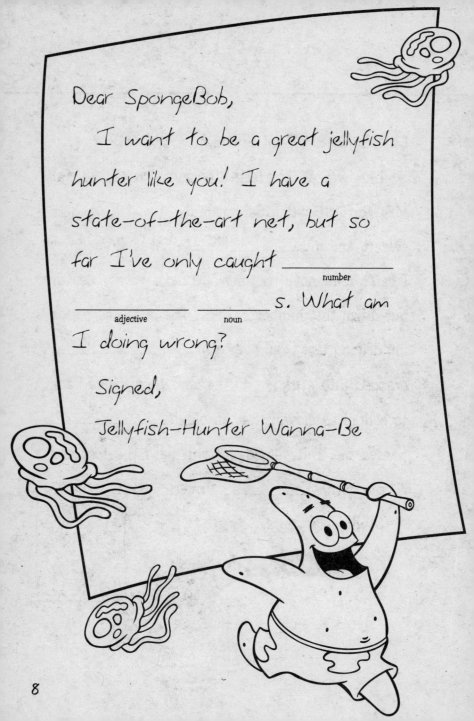

Dear SpongeBob,

I want to be a great jellyfish hunter like you! I have a state-of-the-art net, but so far I've only caught _____
number

_____ _____s. What am
adjective   noun

I doing wrong?

Signed,

Jellyfish-Hunter Wanna-Be

Dear Jellyfish-Hunter Wanna-Be,

You've come to the right place for advice—jellyfishing is my favorite sport! As the great jellyfish hunter

_____ _____ once said: "The
<small>a pet's name</small>   <small>a friend's last name</small>

secret to becoming a(n) _____ jellyfish hunter is
<small>adjective</small>

having the _____ of a(n) _____ ,
<small>body part</small>   <small>type of animal</small>

the heart of a(n) _____ , the eyes of a(n)

_____ , and the strength of a(n) _____ ."
<small>type of insect</small>   <small>type of bird</small>   <small>type of circus performer</small>

I have no idea what that means but it seems to work

for _____ ! It also helps to have a good
<small>same pet's name</small>

battle cry that sounds like a(n) _____ . Just don't get
<small>sound</small>

stung. Once I got stung on my _____ _____
<small>body part</small>   <small>number</small>

times and I couldn't sit down for _____ weeks!
<small>number</small>

Your pal,

SpongeBob
SquarePants

P.S. Don't forget to let the

jellyfish go so you can catch

them again the next day!

9

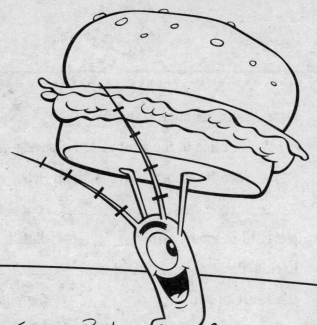

Dear SpongeBob,

    I would like to know how to

make the _____ Krabby Patties.
                 adjective

I promise not to tell anyone the

secret recipe!

    You can trust me,

Joe McSworkelsteen

10

Dear Mr. McSworkelsteen (if that's your real name),

I can never reveal the Krabby Patty recipe! Mr. Krabs made me take the sacred Krabby Patty oath of secrecy: "I swear I will never tell the secret of the Krabby Patties! If I do, may my _____ be tickled and my
_{body part}
_____ be sprayed with hot_____, and
_{body part}   _{type of liquid}
may I soak in a bathtub full of _____ juice
                                                    _{type of vegetable}
and may wild_____s nibble at my toes, and
                           _{type of animal}
may _____ sing_____ in_____
    _{a teacher's name}   _{a song title}   _{foreign language}
over and over till I turn _____and then make me watch
                                    _{color}
_____ movies backward!" So you can understand
_{movie star}
why I would never tell!

Your krabby pal,

SpongeBob
SquarePants

11

Dear SpongeBob,

I am a(n) _____ fan of
adjective

Mermaid Man and Barnacle Boy.

I hear you have a(n) _____
adjective

collection of their things. Can

you tell me about it?

Signed,

Mermaid Man Fan

Dear Mermaid Man Fan,

I have a rare Mermaid Man _____ that
article of clothing

smells like a(n) _____ when you put it in
type of sea creature

_____. I also have the Mermaid Man watch
type of liquid

that doesn't tell time because he never learned how. I

have the Barnacle Boy _____ with _____ spring
noun _adjective_

action that makes it _____ _____ feet per second
verb _number_

(batteries not included). I also have an autographed

Mermaid Man _____ and a Barnacle Boy
bathroom item

_____ that comes in _____ colors and goes
noun _number_

_____ when you throw it. My favorite thing is a piece
sound

of Mermaid Man _____-flavored _____ that is
flavor _food item_

_____ years old and still in perfect condition!
number

Your super friend,

SpongeBob
SquarePants

13

Dear SpongeBob,

I have a friend named SpongeBob
SquarePants! Isn't that _____
                                    adverb
amazing? You both have the same name!
Signed,
Patrick Star

Dear Patrick,

It's me—your best_____ SpongeBob! When I

noun

am not_____ overtime at the Krusty Krab,

-ing verb

I write an advice column for the *Bikini*_____

noun

Times. We just talked about it yesterday, remember?

I told you about the big _____ in my office,

noun

the_____ phone with all the flashing lights,

adjective

and the supply closet that is filled with_____s.

noun

Call me—we'll do lunch!

Best,
SpongeBob

Dear SpongeBob,

My friends invited me to a scary movie but I'm too scared to go. I keep making up excuses like, "Sorry, I have to _____ my _____ —maybe next time." But I'm running out of reasons. What should I do?

verb   noun

Signed,
Scaredy Cat

Dear Scaredy Cat,

Buy a _____-gallon box of popcorn and hide
<high number>

behind it when the movie gets_____scary. The
<adverb>

scariest movie I ever saw was *Attack of the*

_____-Foot _____-Shark Monster. It was about
<number>   <type of fruit>

a shark named _____, who was very nice until
<a boy's name>

a vampire _____ bit him. After that he turned
<type of insect>

into a giant_____ every time the moon rose.
<noun>

His girlfriend,_____, loved him even though he
<a girl's name>

ate her_____, her favorite_____,
<musical instrument>   <noun>

and all the_____s in the city. My friend Patrick
<noun>

hid under his seat the whole time. He missed the

movie, but he found a lot of old _____ on
<type of food>

the floor to snack on.

Your frightened friend,

SpongeBob
ScaredyPants

Dear Mr. SquarePants,

I would like to get a job at the Krusty Krab. I have a lot of experience in fast food. I make excellent _____
type of fruit
and _____ sandwiches, delicious
type of vegetable
fried _____ -balls, and the best
type of food
_____ with seaweed sprinkles this
type of dessert
side of the Pacific. Can you help me?

Sincerely yours,

Mr. P.

Dear Mr. P.,

I am afraid there are no job openings at the
Krusty Krab. No one ever quits because it's the most
_____ job in the world! When I'm _____ Krabby
    adjective   -ing verb
Patties I feel like the king of the_____! And I don't
                                    a place
just get to make the greatest burgers this side of
_____, I get to sweep_____s under the rug,
  a planet   noun
make the bathrooms extra_____, and watch Mr.
                            adjective
Krabs_____his money!
    verb

Your krusty buddy,

**SpongeBob
SquarePants**

19

Dear SpongeBob,

My mom only lets me watch _____ hours of
number

television a day. I want to make sure I'm seeing

the _____ ones. What are your favorite TV
adjective

shows?

Signed,

Couch Potato

Dear Couch Potato,

My very favorite TV show is *Mermaid Man and Barnacle Boy*, but I also like *The_____ Man and*
_{noun}

the_____,   _____ for Sand Dollars,
_{type of fish}   _{·ing verb}

The _____ Adventures of Jed _____
_{adjective}   _{type of fish}

_____, How to _____ Your Snail,
_{type of occupation}   _{verb}

and Everybody Loves _____.
_{type of fish}

Your TV-loving pal,

SpongeBob SquarePants

21

Dear SpongeBob,

There's a bully at school who keeps bothering me. He _____ s me when I walk by, _____ s my lunch money,
_{verb}

and sometimes even stuffs me into a(n) _____ ! What should I do?

Signed,

Hiding in My Locker

Dear Hiding in My Locker,

Bullies are just nice people trapped inside mean

people's _____ s. You could try to win him over by

noun

making him a(n) _____ or by inviting him to

type of dessert

_____ . Or you could do what I do when I see

a place

a bully: _____ away as fast as a(n) _____,

verb _type of animal_

screaming like a(n) _____ !

type of bird

Safe at home,

**SpongeBob
SquarePants**

23

Dear SpongeBob,

Have you ever been to a rodeo? I am very curious about what goes on there. I hear it has something to do with _____ s _____
type of animal   -ing verb
_____ s around a ring. Is that true?
noun

Signed,

Rhinestone Cowboy

Dear Rhinestone Cowboy,

I have never been to a rodeo, but my friend Sandy told me all about them. You wear _____

article of clothing

and chaps and _____ boots with pointy

type of occupation

toes and _____s on the heels. Then you ride a(n)

noun

_____ piggyback yelling 'yee haw' until he

type of animal

_____s you by_____you up and down. The

verb   -ing verb

object is to stay on the _____ for

same type of animal

_____seconds before getting _____across the

number   -ed verb

ring. Sounds _____ to me!

adjective

Yipee Yi Yay,

SpongeBob SquarePants

25

Dear SpongeBob,

What kind of music do you like? I'm tired of all my _____s and would like some new _____s to listen to. Are there any_____s from Bikini Bottom that I should check out?

Signed,

Singing Fool

Dear Singing Fool,

I love music! One of my favorite bands is The

_____ _____ Experience. My
　　type of sea creature　　　　*type of fruit*

favorite songs by them are "_____ in the
　　　　　　　　　　　　　　　a girl's name

_____ with_____s," and "If You Were My_____ I'd
noun　　　*noun*　　　　　　　　　　　　*noun*

_____ with You All Day Long Except_____."
verb　　　　　　　　　　　　　　　*day of the week*

My friend Patrick's favorite band is The_____·Note
　　　　　　　　　　　　　　　low number

Band. They only play _____ note(s) and they only
　　　　　　　　　same number

know one song called "This Song Is Hard to Play." My

friend Sandy loves The Texas_____ Boots (featuring
　　　　　　　　　　　　adjective

Betty Sue_____ on _____). Squidward
　　type of sandwich　　　*musical instrument*

likes The _____-Clarinet Orchestra and Louis
　　　　　high number

_____ and the_____ Hot Clams.
type of fish　　　　　*number*

Musically yours,

**SpongeBob
SquarePants**

27

Dear SpongeBob,

I am throwing a party next week and I want it to be great. We're going to play pin the _____ on the _____ , musical
     noun   type of animal
_____s, and capture the _____ . But
     noun   noun
I need help figuring out what else to do.

Any advice?

Signed,

Party Hearty

Dear Party Hearty,

The secret to a good party is good food, good music, and good friends! My favorite party foods are pizza with_____ and _____ on top,
type of breakfast food   type of candy

_____ cupcakes, and of course, Krabby
type of lunch meat

Patties. I know all the latest dance moves, so if you invite me to your fun party I'll show everyone how to do "The Funky_____," "The _____ _____,"
noun   adjective   noun

and "The _____ Twist." Most importantly, you
type of hat

need good friends at a party! They can help you clean up. And like my friend Patrick always says, "A party without friends is a like a _____ without a(n)
noun

_____ in the_____."
car part   season

Good luck,

SpongeBob SquarePants

29

Dear SpongeBob,

  I'm thinking about getting a pet snail.

Snails are so _____ and _____.
                    adjective   adjective

Can you tell me about your pet snail,

Gary?

Signed,

I Like Gary

Dear I Like Gary,

Gary is _____ special! He's a purebred snail
        adverb

directly descended from _____ , the _____
          a boy's name   *adjective*

snail from the fourteenth century who saved the

_____ Wall of _____ from burning down
adjective   *name of city*

by sliming it. Gary can do _____ tricks! He can
          high number

jump over a(n) _____ , he knows how to say "meow"
      noun

in _____ languages, and he does a perfect imitation
  number

of _____ . Gary and I really like to play
   movie star

hide-and- _____ . I always hide in my _____
      verb   *type of room*

and he always finds me by using his _____ .
                          body part

Gary is the greatest pet a sponge could have!

Your partner in slime,

SpongeBob
SquarePants

31

Dear SpongeBob,

   Guess what? I am in the Mermaid Man and Barnacle Boy Fan Club too! We should meet up at the _____
a place
for a(n) _____ and _____
type of food   type of drink
and swap trading cards. What is your favorite Mermaid Man and Barnacle Boy adventure?

         Signed,
         MM & BB Forever

32

Dear MM & BB Forever,

I love *all* the Mermaid Man and Barnacle Boy Adventures, but my favorite is "Mermaid Man Meets the _____ s of the
type of occupation
_____ Empire of Space Dinosaurs." It's the one where Mermaid
adjective
Man is captured by Man Ray, put in a(n)_____, and sent into
type of pastry
space in a(n)_____. Meanwhile Barnacle Boy can't find Mermaid
noun
Man so he hangs up his_____ and gets a job at a(n)
article of clothing
_____ _____ _____ s. Mermaid Man is
place of work   -ing verb   noun
turned into a(n)_____ and held prisoner inside a_____
noun   type of room
and forced to make_____ s. He escapes using a(n)_____,
type of toy   kitchen item
and a space dinosaur named_____ helps him build a space
a girl's name
ship out of _____ to return home! Mermaid Man finds Barnacle
type of fruit
Boy, who is now selling_____ s door-to-door. The two heroes
noun
are reunited; they capture Man Ray and find out that he is Mermaid

Man's _____ 's _____ 's _____ 's
type of relative   type of relative   type of relative
_____ 's best friend!
type of relative

Up, up, and away!

SpongeBob
SquarePants

Dear SpongeBob,

I keep having the same _____
nightmare about _____
shrinking down to the size of a(n)

_____ and moving into my

_____ drawer. Do you
ever have weird dreams?

Signed,

Dream Weaver

Dear Dream Weaver,

I had a(n)_____ _____ dream last night! I
<small>adverb</small> <small>adjective</small>

lived in an oversized _____ and rode to work on
<small>type of hat</small>

a(n) _____ . But I wasn't working at the
<small>type of animal</small>

Krusty Krab–I had a job at the Chum Bucket! I had to

make plankton patties and sing songs about_____s!
<small>noun</small>

The plankton patties were made out of_____ flakes,
<small>noun</small>

_____ goo, and_____chunks. I ate one and it tasted
<small>noun</small> <small>noun</small>

like a(n)_____ . And then my friends walked in and
<small>noun</small>

they all looked_____weird! Patrick was a(n)_____,
<small>adverb</small> <small>noun</small>

Sandy was a(n)_____ , Squidward was a(n)
<small>type of occupation</small>

_____ , and Gary was a man-eating_____ .
<small>type of plant</small> <small>type of bird</small>

Boy was I glad to wake up!

Sleeping with one eye open,

**SpongeBob
SquarePants**

Dear SpongeBob,

Why are *you* of all people giving advice! I should be doing it! The readers need someone who is _____ smart and _____ intellectual!
_{adverb} _{adverb}
I know about _____ in _____ , where
_{-ing verb} _{a country}
_____ go to _____, and the difference
_{type of fish} _{verb}
between _____s and_____
_{type of vegetables} _{type of dance}
. . . unlike some people I know.

Signed,

Squidward

Dear Squidward,

I would love your help writing these letters! It would be the greatest thing since _____ a famous person went _____ in _____ and discovered the -ing verb   a place first _____. There's plenty of room at my _____ noun   type of furniture for both of us. We could sit side by side and go out for

_____ and eat with our _____ s and take type of food   body part long walks in the _____ together. We'll be joined at noun the _____ –it'll be great! body part

Your *pen* pal,

SpongeBob

Dear SpongeBob,

   I want to get a surprise gift for my best friend. Last year I got him a(n) _____ -flavored _____
   type of fruit   article of clothing
and a pet _____ . What do you
              noun
think he would like? He is yellow and square and spongy.

Thank you,

Patrick Star

P.S. Don't tell SpongeBob I'm getting him a gift! It's a secret!

Dear Patrick,

Thanks pal, but you don't have to get me a gift! Although I did like the _____ made out
type of board game

of_____ you gave me on _____ !
type of candy day of the week

Your friend,

SpongeBob

Dear SpongeBob,

   Is the Flying Dutchman real or imaginary? I made a bet with my friend that he's real. If I win the bet, she has to _____ my _____s until

_____ ; if she wins, I have to _____

        verb   noun

her_____s until_____! Can you

       noun   month

settle our bet?

Signed,

Fingers Crossed

Dear Fingers Crossed,

The Flying Dutchman is as real as a(n)_____!

noun

And so are Santa Claus, the Easter_____,

type of animal

the Tooth _____, and the_____

type of occupation   adjective

_____ that goes_____ in the_____

type of fish   sound   time of day

and brings_____to good little boys and girls!

type of candy

Your best bet,

*SpongeBob
SquarePants*

41

Dear SpongeBob,

You have a(n) _____ sense of
             adjective

style—I just love the _____
                           adjective

fashions you wear. How can I become

a(n) _____ dresser like you?
          adjective

Signed,

Clothes Horse

Dear Clothes Horse,

Everyone should have a white shirt, tie, short pants, athletic socks, and shoes in their wardrobe! But when you play _____ you should wear a(n)

type of sport

_____ , tight _____ pants, and size_____
type of hat color size

sneakers. If you go out on the town to_____
verb

someplace fancy, you should wear a(n)_____
type of flower

in your lapel and carry a(n)_____. And make
noun

sure your shoes are _____ and your socks are
adjective

_____ .
adjective

All dressed up and

nowhere to _____ ,
verb

SpongeBob
SquarePants

43

Howdy, SpongeBob!

How the _____s are you? I'm in Texas right now–the
        noun

_____ place in the world! You would love it here,
  adjective

SpongeBob. They're having a(n) _____ Karate
                                    adjective

Jamboree, a(n) _____ rodeo, and a(n)
                type of insect

_____ festival all in the same week! I'll bring
  type of dance

you a(n) _____-gallon cowboy hat, a giant box
          high number

of hot chili _____s, and some chocolate-covered
              food item

_____s shaped like a Texas _____. Wish
  noun   type of reptile

you were here!

Yee Haw,

Sandy

P.S. Don't forget to water my _____s and feed my
                                noun

_____s.
  noun

Dear Sandy,

That sounds _____! I can't wait to hear all
                    adjective

about your _____ trip! Take lots of _____s
               adjective   noun

and hurry back, y'all!

Your karate-chopping buddy,

SpongeBob

Dear SpongeBob,

I got the lead _____ in my school
                    noun

play "The Importance of Being

_____." I am very nervous!
type of sandwich

Help!

Signed,

Sweaty Palms

Dear Sweaty Palms,

Just relax and don't do what I did! I was in a play at the

Bikini Bottom _____ Theater called "King Neptune
                    type of meal

and the _____ _____." I had to wear a(n)
            adjective   noun

_____ made out of_____ fur. My
    article of clothing   type of animal

sword got tangled in the fur and I tripped and fell on my

_____. I started sweating like a(n)_____.
  body part   type of sea creature

I only had one line: "I have a message for the king in my

pocket that must be sent to France by pigeon." Instead I

said, "I have a(n)_____ for the_____ in my
                    noun   type of occupation

_____ that must to be sent to_____ by
    article of clothing   a planet

a(n)_____." Patrick thought it was the_____
      type of fish   -est adjective

line he'd ever heard.

Your fellow nervous actor,

SpongeBob
SquarePants

Thanks for all of your help

with these letters-so long!

Ever your pen pal,

SpongeBob
SquarePants